The ETHERINGTON BROTHERS

Long Gone DON

BOOK 1

The MONSTROUS UNDERWORLD

LONG GONE DON BOOK 1: THE MONSTROUS UNDERWORLD
is a
DAVID FICKLING BOOK

First published in Great Britain in 2014 by
David Fickling Books,
31 Beaumont Street, Oxford, OX1 2NP

www.davidficklingbooks.com

978 1 910 200 049

DAVID FICKLING BOOKS Reg. No. 8340307

A CIP catalogue record for this book is available from the British Library.

Printed and bound in Great Britain by Polestar Stones

David Fickling Books supports the Forest Stewardship Council (FSC®), the
leading international forest certification organisation. All our titles that are
printed on Greenpeace-approved FSC®-certified paper carry the FSC® logo.

FSC
www.fsc.org

MIX
Paper from
responsible sources
FSC® C015140

The ETHERINGTON BROTHERS' Long Gone DON

This book is dedicated to...

"My son, Calvin, for making every new
day a monstrously grand adventure."
- *Robin*

"Ma, for showing me that an artist
never stops *experimenting* and *learning*,
and Pa, for teaching me to take
pride in making things *properly*."
- *Lorenzo*

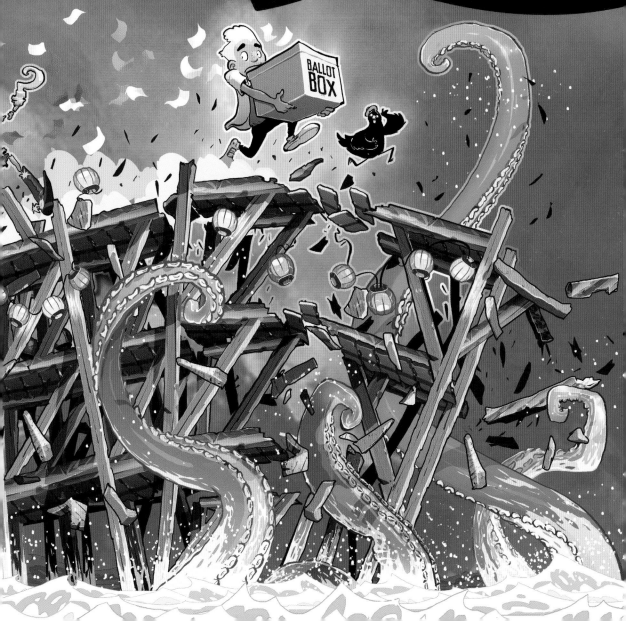

THE REMARKABLE TALE OF **DON SKELTON** BEGINS AT THE VERY END. THIS IS NOT A NORMAL PLACE FOR A STORY TO START... BUT THEN AGAIN, THIS IS **NOT** A NORMAL STORY.

FORTUNA JUNIOR SCHOOL PROVIDED THE UNLIKELY STAGE FOR THE FINAL ACT OF DON'S LIFE, WHEN HE MET A VERY STICKY END FOLLOWING A SERIES OF BIZARRE AND RANDOM EVENTS.

IF PASCAL HAD LOOKED BEFORE HE ROLLED HIS DICE (WHILE PLAYING **BRIGANDS & DRAGONS**) THEN THE DINNER LADY WOULDN'T HAVE TRIPPED AND THROWN THE HOT PAN OF **CUSTARD** THAT LANDED ON **EDDIE'S** BACK...

IF EDDIE HADN'T BEEN STARTLED BY THE HOT CUSTARD, THE **PLAYING CARD** HE THREW WOULD HAVE HIT PAULA (HIS INTENDED TARGET) INSTEAD OF KNOCKING OPEN HER **HAMSTER'S** CAGE DOOR (WHICH SHE'D BROUGHT TO SCHOOL FOR SHOW AND TELL)...

IF PAULA'S HAMSTER HADN'T RUN UP THE **CARETAKER'S** TROUSER LEG HE WOULDN'T HAVE FALLEN OFF HIS LADDER AND LANDED IN THE BIG PILE OF **SICK** (CREATED BY A POORLY FIRST YEAR NAMED BOB)...

AND **IF** PAULA HADN'T THOUGHT THE SICK-COVERED CARETAKER LOOKED LIKE A **GHOST** SHE WOULDN'T HAVE BACKED INTO THE **LADDER**, WHICH TOPPLED ONTO DON'S HEAD AND KNOCKED HIM OUT COLD!

ON **JANUARY 7**TH, HOWEVER, ALL THESE THINGS **DID** HAPPEN, AND POOR DON SKELTON DROWNED IN A BOWL OF OXTAIL SOUP – WHICH SMELT A BIT LIKE A WET DOG.

HIS FATE WAS A STRANGE ONE. BUT FATE WAS NOT YET FINISHED.

FOR THAT WAS WHEN EVENTS TOOK AN EVEN **STRANGER** TURN...

...AS DON WAS ABOUT TO DISCOVER...

WHUH-?

AAARGH!

SKPLOOOTCH!

!?!

GAK! BLUB!

¡HIJOLE! WHAT AN ENTRANCE! OH, I'M GIVING THAT DIVE A BIG **SEVEN!** YOU WOULD'VE SCORED MORE IF I COULD COUNT ANY HIGHER.

YOU'RE A ... A ... A... **A TALKING CROW?!**

WELL SPOTTED. BUT AT THE RISK OF POINTING FEATHERS, I HAVE TO ASK – WHAT EXACTLY ARE **YOU** SUPPOSED TO BE?

ARE YOU JOKING? I'M **DON!** AND I'M A **BOY,** OF COURSE – CAN'T YOU TELL? OR HAVE I GOT SOUP ON MY...

RUB RUB

...FACE?

GAAAAH! MY HAIR! WHAT'S HAPPENED TO MY HAIR?

¡AY, CARAMBA! WE'VE GOT A LIVE ONE HERE...

DEEP BREATHS... DEEEEEEEP BREATHS... COME ON, CHICO, LET'S TAKE A SEAT ON THIS SILLY GREAT SPOON.

...PANT... ...PANT... ...PANT...

EVERY NEW LANDING ON THE **ARRIVAL PLAINS** IS A LITTLE BIT FREAKY. MOST FOLKS GET THE WILLIES FROM THE **GREEN SAND** AND THE REST OF THE SCENERY ...I KNOW *I* DID...

BUT *YOU* FLIPPED OVER YOUR OWN **REFLECTION!** YOU DIDN'T EVEN MENTION THE *GIANT BOWL OF SOUP* YOU USED FOR A CRASH MAT ... WHAT FLAVOUR IS THIS BY THE WAY? **WET DOG?**

...WHEEZE... OXTAIL! ...PANT...

B-BUT I WAS JUST EATING LUNCH... **AT SCHOOL!** AND NOW MY HAIR'S TURNED **WHITE** AND I'M CHATTING TO A **BIRD!**

THERE, THERE – LET IT ALL OUT. I PROMISE THINGS WILL LOOK **MUCH** BETTER IN NO TIME.

PAT PAT

GROOOOOOMPH!

OR THEY MIGHT LOOK A **LOT** WORSE! IT'S PROBABLY A LONG SHOT, BUT DO YOU KNOW HOW TO **FLY?**

NO!

SHAME. WELL, WE'LL JUST HAVE TO DO THIS THE OLD FASHIONED WAY... **RUUUUUUN!**

GRAAAAAHH!

!?!

AM ... AM I **D-D-DREAMING?!** THIS HAS **GOT** TO BE SOME SORT OF A **N-N-NIGHTMARE!**

W-WHAT ARE YOU DOING?!

WHICH PART OF **'RUUUUUUN'** ARE YOU STRUGGLING WITH, DON?

WAIT FOR ME!

WHAT IS GOING ON AROUND HERE, MR CROW?!

SOAP

OH, YOU KNOW, THE **USUAL!** AND THE NAME'S NOT MR CROW - IT'S **CASTANET!** NOW STOP GABBING AND... **DIVE!**

?!

IT'S THROWING **GRAND PIANOS** AT US! WHY ... WHY... **WHY...?!**

KRUNK!

ACTUALLY, IT'S **SPITTING** THEM AT US. BUT FURTHER QUESTIONS CAN WAIT - 'STAYING ALIVE' CAN'T! FOLLOW ME, MUCHACHO, AND DO EXACTLY AS I SAY!

GROOARR!

LEEEEEEFT TURN!

WE'RE **NEVER** GOING TO MAKE IT!

JUMP!

WHAP!

SHUNK!

LIIIIIIIIMBO SLIDE!

CLATTER!

CHUNK! WHUMP! BUMP!

NOW, COVER YOUR HEAD, SHUT YOUR EYES, HOPE FOR THE BEST, AND KISS YOUR **CULO** GOODBYE!!!

WAIT? MY **WHAT?** KISS MY **WHAT** GOODBYE?

WAAAGGGH!

WITH A ROLL OF THUNDER THE DANGER PASSES AND SILENCE DESCENDS...

IS ... IS IT ALL **OVER?** HAS IT **GONE?**

I DON'T UNDERSTAND THIS PLACE AT ALL... **WHY** WOULD THAT THING JUST GIVE UP, MR CASTANET? IT HAD US CORNERED!

NO IDEA, IT'S - *PUFF* - WEIRD LIKE THAT. SEEMS TO ENJOY THE CHASE MORE THAN THE CATCH. ...*HORRIBLE SMELLY GREAT SAND GIT...*

AS FOR **THIS** PLACE, WELL, WE DON'T REALLY HAVE WHAT YOU'D CALL A 'TOURIST INDUSTRY', SO IT'S PRETTY MUCH UP TO ME TO SHOW YOU THE ROPES ... AND HERE'S THE FIRST! **HA!**

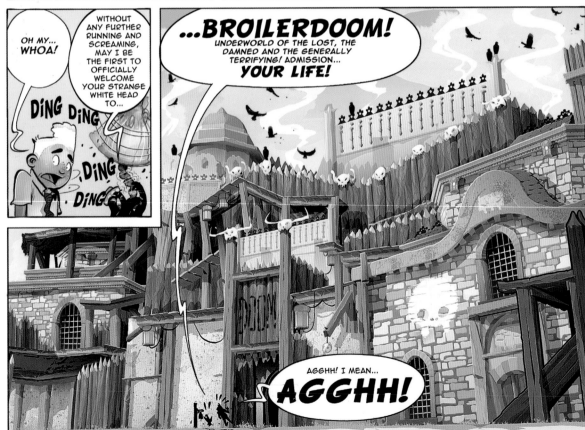

OH MY... **WHOA!**

WITHOUT ANY FURTHER RUNNING AND SCREAMING, MAY I BE THE FIRST TO OFFICIALLY WELCOME YOUR STRANGE WHITE HEAD TO...

DING DING

DING

DING

...**BROILERDOOM!** *UNDERWORLD OF THE LOST, THE DAMNED AND THE GENERALLY TERRIFYING!* ADMISSION... **YOUR LIFE!**

AGGHH! I MEAN... **AGGHH!**

GREAT GOOGALLY GUMBALLS!!

I RECOMMEND STANDING *VERY* STILL. THIS USUALLY ONLY TAKES A MOMENT.

CRASH! WHAM! WUMP! RUMMAGE!

AS THE DUST SETTLES...

COUGH!... HACK!...

YUK... POMEGRANATES AGAIN!

THEY ... THEY TOOK **EVERYTHING!** EVERYTHING EXCEPT MY **CLOTHES!**

I GUESS SOUP-STAINED RAGS AREN'T FETCHING THE PRICE THEY USED TO. STILL SEEMS TO BE A MARKET FOR MY **HAT** THOUGH...

LESSON NUMBER ONE: BROILERDOOM *GIVES* WITH ONE HAND AND *TAKES* WITH THE OTHER. THIS IS AN OPPORTUNIST'S UNDERWORLD, DON, WHICH MEANS IF YOU **THINK** YOU CAN GET AWAY WITH SOMETHING, YOU PROBABLY **CAN!**

STOLEN STUFF

SO PEOPLE JUST KEEP... **STEALING** FROM EACH OTHER?

AH, YOU SOON GET USED TO IT. WATCH AND LEARN. **ONE MINIATURE SOMBRERO, PLEASE!**

NOW, SEÑOR, I DON'T HAVE ANY ACTUAL **MONEY,** BUT I AM PREPARED TO TRADE ... FOR THIS.

EH? BUT DAT'S JUS' A REG'LAR OL' FEATHER!

NO! **THIS** IS A WAND OF ENCHANTMENT, WITH THE POWER TO **TRIPLE** YOUR SALES OVERNIGHT – AND IT'LL HEAL THE PIMPLES ON YOUR WIFE'S NOSE!

SWEET POTATOES, YA GOTS A **DEAL!**

POINK

YOU **FIBBER!** YOU PLUCKED THAT FEATHER FROM YOUR **BUM!**

YEP, AND THAT CROOK JUST TRIED TO SELL ME BACK MY **OWN** – JUST STOLEN – HAT, SO I THINK THINGS WORKED OUT RATHER WELL! NOW, LISTEN UP...

THIS IS THE MAIN SQUARE FOR THE SLUMS. AND YOU'RE IN FOR A TREAT, BECAUSE IT'S **ELECTION DAY!** LET'S GET IN LINE.

DON'T BE SILLY, MR CASTANET. I CAN'T VOTE. I'M JUST A BOY.

SPODE

YOUR VOTE HERE

HERE!

NOT HERE

RIPLEY

SO YOU KEEP SAYING, AMIGO, BUT I'VE NO IDEA WHAT A **BOY** IS! ANYWAY, IT DOESN'T MATTER BECAUSE **EVERYONE** VOTES IN BROILERDOOM. IT'S TRADITION!

TRADITION... LIKE THE WELCOME PARTY?

YEAH, EXACTLY. WELL, THAT AND IT'S THE **LAW!** WE **HAVE** TO VOTE.

VOTING SLIPS

SO, FOR INSTANCE ... I **COULD** VOTE FOR ONE OF THESE TWO WEIRDOS, IF I WANTED TO?

NOPE – YOU **HAVE** TO VOTE, REMEMBER! NOW STAMP A TICKET AND KNOCK YOURSELF OUT. POWER TO THE PEOPLE! ONE CROW, ONE VOTE!

SPODE

YOUR VOTE HERE

HERE!

NOT HERE

RIPLEY

HMMM ... WHY IS EVERYBODY PICKING THAT SPODE FELLOW? THIS RIPLEY LOOKS MUCH MORE FRIENDLY...

COURSE, ONLY A CLUELESS **TOURIST** WOULD CHOOSE **RIPLEY!** ...WAIT A MINUTE...

NOT HERE

NOOOOO!!!

WHAT'S GOING ON? I THOUGHT YOU SAID THIS WAS **OKAY!**

SURE, CHICO – AS LONG AS YOU DON'T PICK **THAT** GUY! GENERAL SPODE'S GOING TO HAVE US STUFFED AND MOUNTED LIKE A PAIR OF NOVELTY PIÑATAS IN NO TIME!

CLANGALANGALANG CLANGALANG GCLA...

CLANGALANGALANGCLANGALANGALANGC

THE WARNING BELLS' CLAMOUR RISES FROM THE MARKET PLACE, RESOUNDING THROUGHOUT THE **KRAPOOKERVILLE** SLUMS...

AS THE NOISE REACHES **THE BRIDGE OF CROSSING**, SPANNING **LOST HOPE MOAT**, IT IS JOINED BY THE ALARM OF THE DUTY GUARD.

CLANG CLANG ALANG ALANG

DING DING ALANG BING DONG DING BONG RING KLANG

A FURTHER RING-A-DING IS ADDED BY THE HIGH LOOKOUT, POSITIONED AMONG THE GILDED ROOFTOPS OF MIGHTY **CORPSE CITY**.

FINALLY, THE ENTIRE TINKLING ORCHESTRA REACHES THE PALACE OF **GENERAL SPODE**, WHO IS NOT, AS IT TURNS OUT, A MUSIC LOVER.

KNOCK THAT RACKET OFF, YOU BRAINLESS GOIT! I DON'T NEED TO HEAR YOU TO SEE WHAT'S GOING ON!

CLANG-A-LANG-A-!!!

B BONK!

A SLUM DWELLER WITH WEIRD HAIR AND A FEATHERED PINCUSHION JUST PLACED A VOTE IN RIPLEY'S BOX! WHICH OF THESE FACTS DO YOU THINK BOTHERS ME THE MOST, **VALUSH?**

WELL, YOU ARE RATHER **BALD**, SPODE, SO I'M GUESSING IT'S THE HAIR.

NO, YOU RAGGED ROGUE - IT'S **ALL** OF THEM! AND THAT'S 'GENERAL' SPODE TO YOU! I EARNED THIS RANK AND I ENJOY HEARING IT SPOKEN!

SIGH ... WHY DON'T YOU TELL ME WHAT'S WRONG, **GENERAL.**

VALUSH, I TRUST YOU WITH SENSITIVE MISSIONS BECAUSE YOU'RE THE BEST AGENT BROILERDOOM HAS TO OFFER. YOU'RE A CUNNING, RUTHLESS, SNEAKY, DOUBLE-DEALING **DEVIL...**

BUT YOU'VE FAILED IN YOUR MOST **VITAL** TASK! NO ONE... NO ONE ... WAS EVER TO CHALLENGE MY RULE OF THIS UNDERWORLD! **NO ONE!!!**

VOTE SPODE

AND YET YOU'VE ALLOWED A NEWCOMER AND A SKINNY **CROW** TO KICK SAND IN MY FACE BY GIVING RIPLEY HIS FIRST VOTE IN A **CENTURY!** SOME DAYS I WONDER WHY I PAY YOU...

I'VE CERTAINLY BEEN WONDERING **WHEN** YOU'LL PAY ME.

WHAT? WHAT WAS THAT? MUTINY IN THE RANKS?! I'VE A MIND TO FEED YOU TO THE **MOAT!!**

TEMPER, TEMPER, SPODEY...

...RAISED VOICES HAVE A NASTY HABIT OF CRIMPING MY HAIRDO, AND **THIS ONE** COST MORE THAN YOUR TELESCOPE.

A THOUSAND APOLOGIES, **REGINA**, MY DEAR CHERUB! I WAS THOUGHTLESS AND STUPID AND OAFISH! HOW CAN YOU EVER FORGIVE ME?

LET ME SEE ... TWO FOOLISH CITIZENS HAVE DARED TO VOTE AGAINST YOU, SPODEY? SUCH **SWEET** RECKLESSNESS MAKES A GIRL HUNGER FOR A LITTLE POWER OF HER OWN... SO YOU'RE GOING TO ALLOW **ME** TO **SOLVE** THIS PROBLEM FOR YOU.

I ORDER YOU TO ASSIGN THE CAPTURE OF THESE CRIMINALS TO THE **SLUM GUARDS**. COUNT VALUSH TENDS TO LEAVE BODIES IN HIS WAKE, AND THE WEATHER IS TOO WARM FOR **CORPSES!**

SAYS *YOU*, MADAME.

VERY WELL, SWEETUMS, IT SHALL BE SO! ANYTHING FOR MY SUGARPLUM FAIRY!

GUARD! YOU MAY NOW RING THE BELL! THE **SPECIAL** BELL!

Y-YESSIR!

AND SO BEGINS ANOTHER UNIQUE DEMONSTRATION OF GENERAL SPODE'S ADVANCED COMMUNICATION NETWORK.

BONG DONG

AND WHILE ALL SUCH TECHNOLOGICAL BREAKTHROUGHS FACE OPPOSITION...

KLONG A-BONG DONG

WHY DO YOU ALWAYS STAND ON *MY* ROOF!

...AND MUST BRIDGE GREAT GAPS IN KNOWLEDGE...

DONG-A BONG-A- MOOOO!

WHAT'S THAT, THEN?

S'MY **COWBELL**, OF COURSE!

...THE BOLD MARCH OF PROGRESS CANNOT BE STOPPED. AND IT DOES *NOT* TAKE PRISONERS.

UP AN' AT 'EM, BOYS! THEY IS PLAYIN' OUR TUNE!

RIGHT THEN, DON, WE'VE TWO CHOICES: (1) WE STAY AND FACE THE **MUSIC!** (2) I GIVE YOU THE **WHISTLE-STOP** TOUR OF MY FAVOURITE ESCAPE ROUTES!

HERE!

NOT HERE

ER, NUMBER TWO, PLEASE, CASTANET! I DON'T LIKE THE **SOUND** OF NUMBER ONE!

IN THE NAME OF OUR DEAR DESPOTIC LEADER, I ARREST YOU TWO VAGRANTS FOR THE CRIME OF *TREASON!* I WOULD READ YOU YOUR RIGHTS ... BUT YOU DON'T 'AVE ANY! HAHA!

I THINK WE'VE GOT OFF ON THE *WRONG* FOOT BECAUSE YOU'RE DEAD *WRONG* TO ROB US OF OUR *RIGHTS.* AFTER ALL, EVERYONE KNOWS TWO WRONGS DON'T MAKE A RIGHT!

I DON'T THINK ARGUING WITH THEM IS GOING TO HELP, MR CASTANET! WE'RE SURROUNDED!

FEAR NOT, DON! WHAT THE SLUM GUARDS LACK IN THE WAY OF *CHARITY*, THEY MAKE UP FOR IN *STUPIDITY*. NOW WAIT FOR MY SIGNAL...

DRAG!

DEVILS, DEMONS AND DUNGBEETLES! LEND ME YOUR HORNS! SHARE WITH ME YOUR WOES!

HOP!

HOW *LONG* HAS IT BEEN SINCE GENERAL SPODE GAVE ANY OF YOU BRAVE SOLDIERS THE DAY OFF? HOW MANY *HOURS* HAVE YOU SPENT PATROLLING IN THE DARK WITH NOTHING BUT A FLAMING TORCH FOR COMPANY?

ER ... LAST TIME I 'AD AN 'OLIDAY WAS BACK WHEN I 'AD ME OWN *TEEF!*

AN' IT'S THREE Y-Y-YEARS SINCE MY T-T-TORCH BURNED OUT. THIS PLACE IS S-S-SCARY AT NIGHT!!

IT DOESN'T *HAVE* TO BE THIS WAY! SIMPLY DECIDE WHAT YOU'D LIKE TO CHANGE ABOUT YOUR JOB, WRITE IT ALL DOWN AND PRESENT YOUR SUGGESTIONS TO SPODE!

WHAT A GOOD IDEA! WE'LL MAKE A LIST!

GREAT! SO WHAT REALLY MATTERS TO YOU BOYS? PSSST! 'LACES' DON...

WINK!

CHOCOLATE BISCUITS IN THE REST ROOM!

'RECYCLED' TOILET PAPER INSTEAD OF 'SECOND-HAND' TOILET PAPER!

REGULAR WEAPON REPAIRS – THIS AXE HAS OVER A THOUSAND KILLS ON THE CLOCK AND IT'S GETTING A LITTLE CHIPPED!

GOOD, GOOD... KEEP GOING...

TANGLE! THE! KNOT!

STAFF PICNICS!

VEGETARIAN OPTIONS IN THE CANTEEN!

WILL YOU LOT PACK THAT IN!!

NEW *TEEF!*

TAP! TAP! TAP!

BUT WHAT ABOUT THE LIST, SARGE...?

FORGET THE LIST!!! WHILE YOU WERE BUSY ARGUIN' OVER WHICH AIR FRESHENER TO 'ANG IN THE GUEST LOO, OUR PRISONERS WERE BUSY *ESCAPIN'!!*

YOU'LL BE EATIN' SECOND-HAND TOILET PAPER IF YOU LOT DON'T GET MOVIN'!

GULP! YES, SARGE! CHARGE!!

HUH?

SNAG!

TUMBLE!

HA – THAT WORKED BRILLIANTLY!

YEP, THE OLD 'TIE-THEIR-LACES-TOGETHER-WHILE-THEY'RE-BUSY-MAKING-A-LIST' RUSE GETS THEM EVERY TIME!

COME BACK HERE!

NOT LIKELY!

THIS IS NOT QUITE THE INTRODUCTION TO THE CITY I INTENDED! THERE WAS A LOT MORE CAKE AND FAR FEWER CUTLASSES IN MY ORIGINAL PLAN!

TICKLE YOUR FANCY (DRESS)

COSTUMES!

OUTFITS!

WHY ARE WE IN SO MUCH TROUBLE? WHAT HAS VOTING FOR THAT RIPLEY GUY GOT TO DO WITH ANYTHING?

?!?

I'LL EXPLAIN THE FINER POINTS OF YOUR MISTAKE SOON, DON, BUT FIRST THINGS FIRST – DISGUISES!

HOLA, MYRTLE! MY NEW FRIEND AND I ARE HAVING A LITTLE TROUBLE WITH THE LONG, SCALY ARM OF THE LAW!

AGAIN, MY DEAR? OH, VERY WELL – HELP YOURSELVES, BUT PLEASE TRY AND BRING BACK WHATEVER YOU BORROW IN ONE PIECE THIS TIME!

HMM ... THIS ALLEY'S TOO G-GLOOMY T-T-TO SEE PROPERLY, SARGE! A N-NEW FLAMING T-T-TORCH, HOWEVER, C-C-COULD PROVE QUITE ILLUMINATIN'!

QUIT YOUR QUIPPING, PRIVATE, AND CHECK EVERY DOORWAY! THEY'RE HERE... I JUST *KNOW* IT!

HURRY UP, DON! I'M GETTING CLAUSTROPHOBIC!

ONE SEC! THERE'S A LOAD OF GREEN SAND IN MY OLD TROUSER POCKETS AND ... AND WHAT'S *THIS?*

CHANGING ROOM

WHERE DID *YOU* COME FROM? WELL, I GUESS A PENDANT IN MY POCKET IS NOT THE STRANGEST THING THAT'S HAPPENED TODAY...

OKAY, SO HOW DO I LOOK?

VERY NATTY, BUT IT'S NOT MUCH OF A DISGUISE. POP THIS OVER YOUR *GLOW-IN-THE-DARK* HAIRDO AND LET'S SKEDADDLE!

SEE? WHAT DID I TELL YOU? THOSE MEAT-BRAINED SLUM GUARDS ARE ABOUT AS USEFUL AS A *WATERPROOF TEABAG*, IF YOU GET MY –

– POINT!?!

ABOUT THIS *LIST* – SHOULD WE POST IT TO SPODE, OR HAND-DELIVER IT FOR THE *PERSONAL* TOUCH?

CASTANET, I'VE ONLY BEEN IN TOWN FIVE MINUTES AND I'VE ALREADY BEEN *CHASED, TERRORISED, MUGGED* AND *SHACKLED!* IS THERE ANYONE, AND I DO MEAN *ANYONE*, WHO MIGHT ACTUALLY WANT TO HELP US?

?!

BAF!!

YOU CALLED?

IT'S ... IT'S ... IT'S
L-L-LEWD!!!

MY FRIENDS CALL ME 'LEWD'. MY BANK MANAGER CALLS ME 'MR LEWD, SIR' AND MY MUM CALLS ME 'LIDDLE WIDDLE LEWDY'...

...AND YOU ARE **NONE** OF THE ABOVE!!

PLAF!

HE REALLY IS LEWD!

YEP. LEWD'S A FIRM BELIEVER IN THE REGULAR AND TIMELY USE OF 'COLOURFUL' VOCABULARY.

DUMPF!

THE STANDARD OF MILITARY TRAINING THESE DAYS IS SHOCKING...

CLONK!

BOFF!

WHAT ARE YOU IDIOTS **DOIN'**?! STOP GETTIN' KNOCKED OUT AND **GRAB HIM!!**

...ITEM (7): A FULLY S-S-STOCKED MEDICINE C-CABINET...

I'M JUST ABOUT FINISHED HERE, **SAFINA!** YOU CAN FREE OUR TWO REBELLIOUS FRIENDS WHENEVER YOU'RE READY!

SLAPPY! SLAP! SLAP! SLAP!

ALREADY DONE.

?

?!

CLATTER!

¡DIOS MÍO! MY POOR FEATHERS!

HOW DID YOU MANAGE TO –

STEEL-REINFORCED, 18-TOOTH, LEAF-SPRUNG 'HATE' SHACKLES WITH THE BACKLOADING QUICK CUFF SYSTEM ... I COULD PICK THOSE BLINDFOLDED WITH BOTH HANDS TIED BEHIND MY BACK...

...THE REAL QUESTION IS, WHY COULDN'T A TROUBLEMAKER OF YOUR REPUTATION DO THE SAME?

TOK!

RUB! RUB!

SETTLE DOWN, GIRL. CAN'T YOU SEE HE'S BEEN THROUGH A LOT?

I HAVE! I REALLY HAVE! JUST LOOK AT MY HAIR!

WELL, DON'T YOU WORRY ANY FURTHER. WE'RE HERE TO ESCORT YOU BOTH TO A SAFE HOUSE.

N-NOWHERE ISH SHAFE FOR YOU C-CRIMINALSH! WE'LL 'UNT YOU D-DOWN! YOU M-MUSHT OBEY GENERAL SHPODE –

SORRY, BUT WHERE WE'RE GOING WE DON'T NEED SPODE...

YOIP!

BONK!

AND SO THE INTREPID FOURSOME MAKE THEIR WAY ACROSS THE SPRAWLING KRAPOOKERVILLE SLUMS, CASTANET NEVER MISSING A CHANCE TO SHARE HIS LOCAL KNOWLEDGE WITH DON...

...THERE'S THE DEN OF GRUBBY THIEVES! GREAT FOR TIPS OF THE TRADE, BUT YOU'LL WANT A LOOONG BATH AFTERWARDS...

CASTANET, LEAVE DON ALONE AND KEEP QUIET.

...AND THAT'S SILUS CRUPSTUBBLE'S BIZARRE GUITAR BAZAAR! STRANGE-SHAPED INSTRUMENTS ARE HIS SPECIALITY...

WHAT DID I JUST SAY, CASTANET? PUT A SOCK IN YOUR BEAK OR YOU'LL HAVE TO DEAL WITH LEWO!

PSST ... AND IF YOU'RE FEELING PECKISH – AND YOU TIME IT JUST RIGHT – OLD MADAM SUPPY OFTEN LEAVES A LARGE UNATTENDED APPLESAP PIE COOLING ON THAT WINDOW SI –

WHAM!

– S-S-SORRY, L-L-LEWD!

THE JOURNEY THEN PROGRESSES IN PEACE AND QUIET UNTIL...

HERE WE ARE AT LAST! HOME, SWEET HOME!

THIS IS WHERE YOU **LIVE**?

OKAY, I'LL ADMIT SHE'S A LITTLE ROUGH AROUND THE EDGES, BUT **THE DEMON DRINK** IS THE FINEST TAVERN IN TOWN!

ERR ... AND IT'S SAFE, RIGHT? YOU SAID IT WAS **SAFE**!

The Demon Drink
CURES WHAT ALES YOU!

CRASH!

WELL, 'SAFE' MIGHT BE TOO STRONG A TERM...

EVENING, GRONK! HOW'S TRICKS?

OH, CAN'T COMPLAIN, LEWD, CAN'T COMPLAIN.

ANOTHER LIVELY NIGHT AT THE DEMON! I'D BEST SORT OUT THIS SCRAP...

COME ON, AMIGO, THE FIRST DRINK IS ON ME!

NO **WAY!** LAST TIME I FOLLOWED YOU SOMEWHERE DANGEROUS IT DID NOT END WELL!

IT'S YOUR CHOICE, DON. BUT WHEN YOU FANCY LEARNING **HOW** YOU'VE MANAGED TO BECOME THE MOST WANTED CREATURE IN ALL OF BROILERDOOM, I'LL BE WAITING *INSIDE*!

STUPID SOLDIERS OR LOONY LOCALS? **GULP!** DECISIONS, DECISIONS...

I KNOW I'M GOING TO REGRET THIS...

YEEESH!!

HOW CAN YOU BE SO CALM, CASTANET? YOU'RE SURROUNDED BY WEIRDOS AND THERE'S A HUGE PUNCH UP GOING ON BEHIND US! WHAT ARE THEY EVEN FIGHTING ABOUT?

YOU DON'T REALLY NEED REASONS IN THE DEMON. JUST A LOUD VOICE, LARGE FISTS AND A STRONG JAW.

MY NOSE IS NOT BIGGER THAN YOURS!

IT WILL BE IN A SECOND!

TIME TO TAKE IT OUTSIDE, LADS. I NEED THE BAR FOR A MEETING.

PAFF!

BONG!

KONK!

PFFFT... BROILERDOOM IS EXHAUSTING!

TODAY HAS BEEN A BIT ON THE HECTIC SIDE. BUT I'VE GOT JUST THE CURE FOR YOUR TROUBLES.

WHAT IS THIS? IT SMELLS LIKE MOULDY SOCKS!

THIS, DON, IS KNOWN AS A PICK-YOU-UP-PUT-YOU-DOWN! DRINKS SUCH AS THESE ARE WHAT MAKE LIFE SO MUCH FUN! GLUG!

HRGGGURGLE!

BURRRD!!

HUH? THIS IS JUST WARM APPLE JUICE!

...I DUNNO WHAD ISH CALLED BUT IT'SH GOT A KICK LIKE A MULE WEARIN' STEEL-TOED BOOTSH!

YOU KNOW, I NORMALLY DRINK ABOUT A CARTON OF THIS EVERY DAY.

DON'T TALK CRAZY, CHICO! THERE'S QUITE ENOUGH OF THAT GOING AROUND ALREADY!

I'M GLAD YOU DECIDED TO JOIN US, DON. IT'S NOT WISE TO WALK THE SLUMS AFTER DARK. ESPECIALLY WITH HAIR AS BRIGHT AS YOURS.

YEAH, HA, THAT MUCH I'VE DISCOVERED! UM, YOU WERE PRETTY AMAZING BACK THERE, MISS...

SAME AGAIN, PLEASE, MARROW...

MY NAME'S SAFINA. I WAS NEW HERE ONCE, BUT NOW I STEAL FROM THE BULLIES. TAKE THIS MAP, FOR INSTANCE. IT USED TO HANG ABOVE GENERAL SPODE'S FAVOURITE GOLD TOILET!

LISTEN TO ME CAREFULLY, DON. YOU NEED TO KNOW YOUR WAY AROUND TOWN, OR YOU'LL WAKE UP AS SOMETHING'S **BREAKFAST!**

THE DEMON DRINK IS **HERE**, IN THE GRUBBY HEART OF **KRAPOOKERVILLE!** THIS SHANTYTOWN IS HOME TO THE MOST VILLAINOUS, DEADLY, IDIOTIC, GREEDY, MONSTROUS SCUM I'VE EVER KNOWN ... BUT AT LEAST THEY STILL HAVE **RULES!**

AND THIS IS **CORPSE CITY!** INSIDE THESE HIGH WALLS LIVES EVERY KNOWN SHADE OF BACK-STABBING, TWO-FACED, SILVER-TONGUED, WAR-MONGERING, SELL-THEIR-GRANNY-FOR-A-BAG-OF-SWEETS, **SLIME!**

THE UNENDING FOG

CORPSE CITY

KRAPOOKERVILLE

ARRIVAL PLAINS

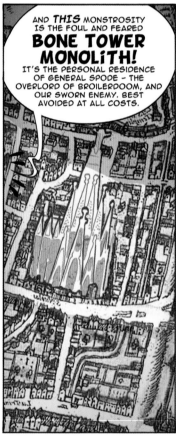

AND **THIS** MONSTROSITY IS THE FOUL AND FEARED **BONE TOWER MONOLITH!** IT'S THE PERSONAL RESIDENCE OF GENERAL SPODE – THE OVERLORD OF BROILERDOOM, AND OUR SWORN ENEMY. BEST AVOIDED AT ALL COSTS.

GULP... AHA! RIGHT! NOW THIS TOWER... IT'S, ER, NOT **REALLY** MADE OF BONES IS IT?

THE RESIDENTS OF KRAPOOKERVILLE HAVE **MANY** REASONS FOR DESPISING SPODE, AND WHENEVER WE THINK WE'RE RUNNING LOW, HE INVENTS A NEW ONE.

BRAVE RESISTANCE FIGHTERS! I HEREBY CALL THIS SECRET MEETING OF THE 'IRREGULARS' TO ORDER! **VIVE LA RÉVOLUTION! DOWN WITH SPODE!!**

SECRET? BUT WHAT ABOUT ALL THE OTHER CUSTOMERS?

I ASKED POLITELY FOR THEM TO LEAVE, BUT THEY DIDN'T SEEM INTERESTED, SO I MOVED TO PLAN 'B' WHICH WORKED RATHER WELL.

AS YOU MIGHT HAVE GUESSED, LEWD IS THE **MUSCLE** OF THE IRREGULARS.

DOES PLAN **'B'** STAND FOR **BREAK BARSTOOL OVER BONCE?** MWAHAHA!

IF I HADN'T HEARD THAT BEFORE, I'D LAUGH. BUT I HAVE, SO I WON'T. DON, MEET **VIKTOR RIKTUS,** THE SMARTEST PILE OF TENTACLES IN ALL THE UNDERWORLD, AND THE BRAINS BEHIND OUR LITTLE OPERATION!

ER, HELLO... **SIR?**

SHAKE SQUELCH

T'WAS **ME** THAT SENT THAT DAFT BIRD OUT TO MEET YOU. I **SENSED** YOUR ARRIVAL!

REALLY? HOW?

I FELT IT IN MY KNEES!

BUT ... BUT YOU HAVEN'T **GOT** ANY KNEES!

YEP, OLD VIKTOR KNOWS HIS STUFF, BUT HE'S A TOUCH ON THE CRAZY SIDE. IT'S FUNNY HOW **REALLY** SMART FOLKS ARE OFTEN A BIT PECULIAR...

GOOD, RIGHT ... NO, HANG ON! IF GENERAL SPODE IS SO HORRIBLE, AND YOU LOT AND **EVERYONE** ELSE CLEARLY HATE HIM SO MUCH, WHY HASN'T THE GUY I VOTED FOR JUST TAKEN OVER?

AH, THAT'S WHERE THINGS GET **COMPLICATED.** RIPLEY **IS** STILL THE KING OF KRAPOOKERVILLE. IF HE **WANTED** TO HE COULD UNITE THE SLUMS TOMORROW AND SAVE YOU FROM SPODE'S WRATH.

BUT AFTER A CENTURY OF BEING IGNORED BY BROILERDOOMIANS, OUR ONE AND ONLY HOPE HAS RETIRED FROM THE HERO BUSINESS AND BEGUN A NEW CAREER ... AS A **CELEBRITY GARDENER!**

TROWEL AND ERROR VOL. 6 - CONQUERING CUCUMBERS! (REVISED EDITION)

AND WITHOUT RIPLEY WHAT REMAINS OF YOUR PRECIOUS IRREGULARS, LEWD? **BRAINS, BRAWN, BURGLAR** AND **BIRD.** OH, AND LET'S NOT FORGET...

...BEAUTY!

THIS TRULY IS AN HONOUR! DON, THE DIVINE CREATURE IN THE SHADOWS IS *REGINA MAGENTA* — OUR SECRET SPY INSIDE CORPSE CITY AND *YOUR* SAVIOUR. REGINA TOLD US OF YOUR TROUBLES.

YOU WONDERFUL THING! NO ONE SINCE RIPLEY HAS EVEN *DREAMED* OF STANDING UP TO SPODE! NO ONE... UNTIL *YOU!*

REGINA, *YOU* ORGANISED THE RESCUE? WOW... I MEAN, THANKS! I JUST WISH YOUR FRIEND THE GARDENER WAS AS HELPFUL.

YES ... I WON'T LIE TO YOU, IT WAS A MAJOR BLOW TO THE RESISTANCE WHEN RIPLEY HUNG UP HIS SWORD AND PICKED UP A SPADE!

SMART MOVE IF YOU ASK ME! HIS BUTTERED PARSNIPS ARE *SUBLIME!*

HA. EVEN *THIS* BOOK'S BEEN SIGNED.

YOU ALL SOUND LIKE YOU'VE GIVEN UP, BUT I ONLY JUST GOT HERE, AND *I'M THE ONE BEING HUNTED!* PERHAPS I CAN CONVINCE YOUR FRIEND TO REJOIN THE REVOLUTION!

HE'S MORE INTERESTED IN *FIGS* THAN *FIGHTING*... BUT THE BIRD KNOWS THE WAY TO HIS GARDEN. STAY OUT OF TROUBLE AND WHEN YOU'RE DONE CHASING LOST CAUSES, WE'LL FIND YOU A GOOD PLACE TO HIDE.

THANKS, SAFINA. OH, AND, UM, THIS IS FOR YOU. IT'S NOTHING SPECIAL, I JUST WANTED TO SAY THANKS FOR, YOU KNOW, SAVING MY LIFE AND EVERYTHING.

?

LET'S GO, CASTANET! ER, WHY ARE YOU BRINGING THAT BOOK?

TO GET IT SIGNED AGAIN, *ESTÚPIDO!* RIPLEY'S PUT HIS NAME IN EVERY COPY IN TOWN BUT A BOOK WITH *TWO* SIGNATURES ... WELL, THAT'S GOTTA BE WORTH SOMETHING, RIGHT?

THE FRANTIC ANTICS OF THE AFTERNOON ARE SOON SOOTHED BY A GENTLE EVENING BREEZE. A PINK UNDERWORLD SUNSET GUIDES OUR HEROES TOWARDS THE RESPLENDENT RIPLEY RESIDENCE...

SWEET SUGAR LUMPS! SAFINA WAS WRONG — THAT'S NOT A GARDEN ... IT'S A *JUNGLE!*

DON'T SAY *JUNGLE*, DON! JUNGLE MEANS *PARROTS*, AND ME AND PARROTS DO *NOT* SEE EYE TO EYE!

ER, **HELLO?** IS ANYONE UP THERE?

IF YOU HEAR AN ECHO, THAT'S A **PARROT** TRICK, AND I'M LEAVING! I SWEAR THEY'RE ALL OUT TO GET ME...

WILL YOU RELAX? I'M NERVOUS ENOUGH ALREADY!

GOOD EVENING, DOWN BELOW! ARE YOU LOST?

YES I AM... I'M REALLY, REALLY, **REALLY** LOST!

PERHAPS I CAN BE OF SOME ASSISTANCE. GRAB A VINE AND COME ON UP.

THIS IS OBVIOUSLY A SILLY QUESTION, BUT WOULDN'T IT BE EASIER FOR YOU TO JUST **FLY?**

¡HIJOLE! I'VE GOT PARROTS ON THE BRAIN AND A HEAVY BOOK UNDER MY WING! NOW IS **NOT** THE TIME TO GET INTO THAT!

ONE SHORT CLIMB, ONE MEDIUM AUTOGRAPH AND ONE LONG EXPLANATION LATER...

...AND HERE WE ARE!

HMMM...

DON, THANKS TO YOUR KIND VOTE, YOU'VE DEFIED SPODE, AND PERFORMED AN ACT, HOWEVER SMALL, THAT NO BROILERDOOMION HAS HAD THE COURAGE TO ATTEMPT. **ALL ON YOUR FIRST DAY IN TOWN!**

HE'S GOT A WEIRD-LOOKING HEAD BUT HE'S A FAST LEARNER! WOW ... TWO SIGNATURES...

NOW, I HATE TO DISAPPOINT BRAVE CREATURES ... AND YET I'M STILL GOING TO. I'M SORRY, DON – YOU'RE ON YOUR OWN.

BUT, BUT WHAT ABOUT **SPODE?!** HAVEN'T YOU SPENT YOUR **ENTIRE LIFE** TRYING TO GET RID OF HIM?

I HAD. BUT THAT WAS BEFORE I **PRUNED** AND **WEEDED** THE WARRIOR SPIRIT FROM MY SOUL, AND CAST IT ONTO THE **COMPOST HEAP** OF REGRET.

I BEG YOUR PARDON?

IT MEANS I DON'T **FIGHT** ANY MORE, LITTLE WHITE HAIR. MINE IS NOW A PEACEFUL SAGE-FILLED EXISTENCE.

RUFFLE

WELL, THAT'S JUST **GREAT.** MEANWHILE, HOW AM I SUPPOSED TO STAND UP AGAINST A **LOONY GENERAL** AND HIS ARMY?!

SPODE IS A **BULLY,** DON, AND THE ONLY WAY TO DEAL WITH A BULLY IS MAKE THEM LOOK STUPID IN FRONT OF THEIR FRIENDS. OH, AND REMEMBER, THE SIMPLEST PLANS ARE ALWAYS THE **BEST!**

AND SO...

...TO WHICH OI SAID, 'PULL THE OTHER ONE – IT'S A SPRING-LOADED CROSSBOW!'

BWAHA HAHAHA!

I KNOW WHAT RIPLEY SAID, BUT I'M HAVING SOME DOUBTS.

HOW CAN THIS FAIL? I SAW IT WORK IN A COMIC! IT'S **FOOLPROOF!**

PAINT

PAINTING A **MOUSTACHE** ON THE GIANT POSTER OF GENERAL SPODE WHICH HANGS FROM THE CORPSE CITY BATTLEMENTS IS NOT **FOOLPROOF,** ESÉ. IT'S JUST **PROOF** WE'RE **FOOLS.**

NO, IT'S AWESOME **PROPAGANDA!** TOMORROW, THE **WHOLE UNDERWORLD** WILL BE LAUGHING AT SPODE AND HE'LL FORGET WHY HE WAS EVER CHASING ME! THERE IS JUST ONE **TINY WRINKLE...**

PAINT

HOW ARE WE GOING TO GET UP **THERE?**

DON, IN BROILERDOOM, THERE'S **ALWAYS** A WAY. WE JUST HAVEN'T FOUND IT YET.

OKAY. THINK, BIRDBRAIN, THINK... **LEVITATION?** TOO UNPREDICTABLE. **TELEPORTATION?** TOO EXPENSIVE. **FLYING?** NO, THAT'S JUST **RIDICULOUS...**

ER, CASTANET, WHAT IS **THAT** HORRIBLE THING?

I THOUGHT THERE'D BE A **LADDER**... A HANDHOLD... **SOMETHING!**

HUH?

LAP!
LAP!

OH, THAT'S A **BRICK-LICKER.** RIPLEY WROTE ALL ABOUT THEM IN HIS CHAPTER 'PESKY PESTS AND VILE VERMIN'. HE EVEN **DISSECTED** ONE – WANNA SEE?

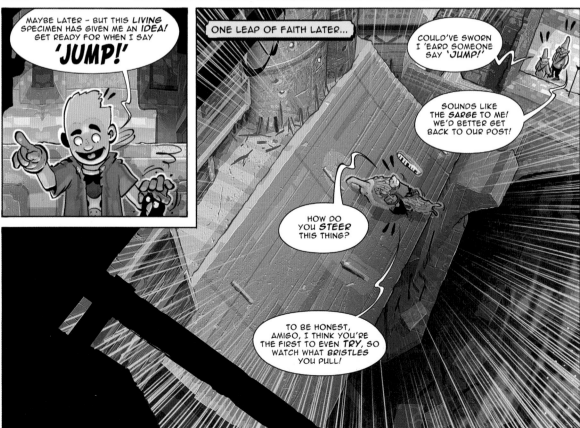
MAYBE LATER – BUT THIS **LIVING** SPECIMEN HAS GIVEN ME AN **IDEA!** GET READY FOR WHEN I SAY **'JUMP!'**

ONE LEAP OF FAITH LATER...

COULD'VE SWORN I 'EARD SOMEONE SAY 'JUMP!'

SOUNDS LIKE THE **SARGE** TO ME! WE'D BETTER GET BACK TO OUR POST!

HOW DO YOU **STEER** THIS THING?

TO BE HONEST, AMIGO, I THINK YOU'RE THE FIRST TO EVEN **TRY**, SO WATCH WHAT **BRISTLES** YOU PULL!

POOOEY! WHAT IS IT EATING? FUNGUS? DIRT?

LAP! LAP!

UM, NO. ACCORDING TO RIPLEY ... THAT'S **PURE EVIL!** UNLIKE THE BRICK-LICKER, I'D TRY NOT TO GET ANY ON YOUR FACE.

THANKS FOR THE WARNING! HEY NOW, WOULD YOU TAKE A LOOK AT THAT – WE MADE IT!

HA! MY DISGUISE TRICK MIGHT NOT HAVE FOOLED THE SLUM GUARDS, BUT YOU REALLY MUST LEARN TO TRUST ME, DON! I SAID THINGS WOULD WORK THEMSELVES OUT...

...AND THEY **HAVE!**

HOORAY!

! !

DROP!

OOOPS!

¡HÍJOLE! I LOST MY DOUBLE-SIGNED BOOK! OH, AND NOW WE'VE GOT A BIG POT OF PAINT BUT NO BRUSH.

THAT'S NOT STRICTLY TRUE. ERM, YOU DID SAY I SHOULD TRUST YOU, RIGHT? THAT IN THIS UNDERWORLD THERE IS **ALWAYS** A WAY?

SORRY, CASTANET, IF THERE WAS ANY *OTHER* SOLUTION I'D BE HAPPY TO GIVE IT A GO, BUT...

FLAP! FLAP! FLAPPETY!

?!

SPLUTCH!

OH, THE INDIGNITY OF BEING USEFUL...

SQUIIIIINK!

RIIIIP!

UH-OH! THE BANNER'S TEARING! WE'RE GOING TO FALL!

REALLY? I'M FEELING PRETTY LOW AS IT IS!

SHRIIIK!

AAAGH!

JUMP, DON, **JUMP!!** BEFORE WE HIT THE MOAT!

WHAT'S THE PROBLEM? IT'S NO WAY **NEAR** AS HIGH AS MY DIVE INTO THAT BIG BOWL OF SOUP! THE WATER WILL CATCH US **AND** CLEAN YOUR FEATHERS!

WATER?! THAT'S **LOST HOPE MOAT!** WHEN YOU FALL IN THERE YOU DO **NOT** GO 'SPLOSH', YOU GO...

SkReEEEee!!

WAAHH!!

RRRip!

Yoip!

WELL, THAT'S THE END OF THAT. ADIOS, CRUEL AFTERLIFE...

SNAG!

HOPE I HAVEN'T **CAUGHT** YOU AT A BAD TIME, BUT I'M AFRAID GENERAL SPODE REQUESTS THE PLEASURE OF CHOOSING YOUR **END** HIMSELF!

THE NEXT MORNING, IN THE BOWELS OF CORPSE CITY. THE LUCKY TENANTS OF **MIDDEN PRISON** ARE ABOUT TO EXPERIENCE THE LATEST REHABILITATION TECHNIQUE – ONE DESIGNED TO PERMANENTLY LOWER THE CRIME RATE...

RISE AN' SHINE, YOU 'ORRIBLE 'ORRORS! IT'S 'GREAT-BIG-GROUP-EXECUTION' DAY!

AN' 'OW DID MY *EXTRA* SPECIAL GUESTS ENJOY THEIR LODGIN'S? EVERYTHIN' TO YOUR FANCY?

IN A WORD, *NO!* THE MATTRESS HAD *LEGS* AND THE TOILET WAS FULL OF *BONES!*

I'M AFRAID THERE'S BEEN A TERRIBLE MIX UP! I'M NOT SUPPOSED TO BE HERE ... I DON'T EVEN KNOW WHERE '*HERE*' IS!

AND EVEN IF WE *ARE* GUILTY, I STILL DEMAND A LAWYER! I HAVE A DEFENCE TO *INVENT!*

MY *TRUNCHEON'S* ALL THE DEFENCE YOU'LL FIND ROUND 'ERE. LET'S SEE WHICH OF YOU IS BEST PREPARED!

NO THANK YOU, THAT WON'T BE NECESSARY. ER, SHALL WE GET GOING?

YOU CHANGED YOUR TUNE IN A HURRY!

PICK YOUR BATTLES, DON. *WOODEN CLUB WITH NAILS* BEATS *INCARCERATED QUICK-TALKING BEAK*, EVERY TIME. AND THAT'S A FACT!

TWENTY PRISONERS AT ONCE! GENERAL SPODE IS SETTING A NEW RECORD TODAY, AND *YOU TWO* WILL HAVE PRIDE OF PLACE! JUST STEP THIS WAY, GENTLEMEN, YOUR AUDIENCE AWAITS...

TA.. TRAAALAALA! TA.. TRAAALAALA!

FLARP!

GENTLE BROILERDOOMIANS! PLEASE PUT YOUR HANDS TOGETHER FOR TODAY'S MAIN ACT - THE KRAPOOKERVILLE CRIMINAL UNDERCLASS IN: 'DROP TILL YOU STOP'!

OOOOOOH, BIG CROWD!

YOU ALMOST SOUND PLEASED!

CLAP CLAP CLAP CLAP

SNIFF ... IF MY MUM COULD SEE ME NOW! WALKING THROUGH CORPSE CITY, PEOPLE CLAPPING AS I PASS ...SNUFFLE... SHE'D BE SO PROUD!

FOR THE LAST TIME, IF YOU MORONS DON'T STOP FUSSING WITH MY ROBES I'LL ADD YOU TO THE LINEUP!!

APOLOGIES, GENERAL! WE JUST WANT TODAY TO BE PERFECT!

THANKS TO COUNT VALUSH AND HIS CROOK-CATCHING NET, IT ALREADY IS! THESE TWO FLEA-BITTEN CURS HAVE CAUSED ME GREAT SUFFERING!

BOOT-KISSING POLITICIANS, JEALOUS RIVALS AND GENERAL MINIONS! TODAY WE PASS SENTENCE ON A BRAZEN BRACE OF COWARDLY CROOKS!

THE FOULEST, MOST HORRIFIC VILLAINS EVER TO MUDDY OUR STREETS WITH THEIR MUCKY PAWS!

MY WORD, OLD SPODE'S LAYING IT ON A BIT THICK, EH?

A 'BIT THICK' IS ONE WAY TO DESCRIBE THE GENERAL...

BUT WHERE IS THE EVIDENCE, I HEAR YOU CRY? IF I MAY DIRECT YOUR ATTENTION FIRST TO EXHIBIT 'A' ... A VOTE FOR RIPLEY, CAST BY THE WHITE-HAIRED DEMON!

BALLOT BOX

EXHIBIT A

JUST ONE VOTE? OOOH, THE CHEEK OF IT!

HEHEHEHE!

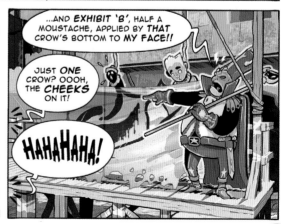

...AND EXHIBIT 'B', HALF A MOUSTACHE, APPLIED BY THAT CROW'S BOTTOM TO MY FACE!!

JUST ONE CROW? OOOH, THE CHEEKS ON IT!

HAHAHAHA!

ERM, YES, THAT IS ALL TRUE! BUT ... BUT PERHAPS IF YOU HEARD *OUR* SIDE OF THE STORY, YOU'D REALISE THIS HAS ALL BEEN A BIG, SILLY MISUNDERSTANDING! AHA!

REBELLIOUS ROGUE! YOU SEEM TO BE CONFUSING THIS GATHERING WITH A *COURTROOM!*

WELL, IT DOES SORT OF SOUND LIKE YOU'RE ACCUSING US OF A CRIME!

THERE'S NO JUSTICE LIKE *INJUSTICE!*

SPODE WOULD NEVER RISK A *HUNG JURY* AT A HANGING. THAT'D BE A PAIN IN THE NECK.

GRRR! I DON'T KNOW *WHO* OR *WHAT* YOU ARE, AND I DON'T CARE! THIS IS *MY* UNDERWORLD, AND I WILL *NOT SHARE IT!!!*

MY NAME IS *DON*, I'M A *BOY* AND WE'VE ONE THING IN COMMON AT LEAST - I DON'T WANT TO LIVE IN YOUR SMELLY UNDERWORLD, YOU *MEAN OLD GOAT!!*

SUCH FOUL INSOLENCE!!! I HEREBY FIND YOU TWO MANGY VILLAINS GUILTY ON ALL COUNTS! YOUR SENTENCE IS... *DEATH!!*

OOOOH, JUST *ONE* DEATH. CAN'T YOU TURN THE OTHER CHEEK?

BWAHAHAHA!

WILL SOMEONE ARREST THAT IDIOT WITH THE CHEEKY DISPOSITION!?!

IT'S THE GALLOWS FOR YOU, MY LAD!

B-BUT MY T-TONGUE WAS F-FIRMLY IN MY CHEEK!!

MY, MY, THINGS *ARE* LOOKING GLOOMY! DO YOU HAVE ANY LAST REQUESTS BEFORE I PULL THIS SHINY LEVER AND WATCH YOU DANCE A SAD LITTLE JIG?

ER, YES ..., YES, I'VE A QUESTION. ARE THESE ROPES *ARROW-PROOF?*

OF COURSE THEY'RE NOT! WELL, IF THAT'S EVERYTHING...

CASTANET?! WE'RE ABOUT TO BE HANGED AND *THAT'S* YOUR FINAL THOUGHT?! YOU PICKED A FINE TIME TO GO *MAD!!*

THWIPP!

MY BEST HAT!

URK!

SWEET SHERBERT DIBDABS!

SHINK!

SNIK...

THUD.

POST HANGING CELEBRATION GROG! THE STRONG STUFF!

GAH! I KNOW WE'RE UNPOPULAR AROUND HERE, BUT HOW COULD YOU POSSIBLY GUESS THAT SOMEONE WAS GOING TO SHOOT ARROWS AT US?

BECAUSE THAT IS EXACTLY THE SORT OF THING SHE LIKES TO DO!

IN CASE YOU TWO ARE FEELING PARTICULARLY STUPID, THIS IS A RESCUE!

GUAAAAAAARDS! CLAP THAT FLAGRANT, FLAME-THROWING FLIBBERTIGIBBET IN IRONS! SHE OWES ME TWO NEW NOOSES!

AND A HAT.

WELL, IF WE'RE REALLY KEEPING SCORE, I'M ABOUT TO OWE YOU A LOT MORE THAN THAT! FLAMING ARROW PLUS BARREL OF GROG EQUALS...

KABOOOOOOM!

WHOOOA!

DOOOOOOF! GAHH!

ARE YOU ALL RIGHT, GENERAL?

PFFFT! WHY, YES, VALUSH. EVERYTHING SEEMS TO BE PERFECTLY FINE DOWN HERE. AND HOW ARE YOU?

NOT TOO GOOD. THAT MINX SHOT A HOLE THROUGH MY HAT.

YOUR HAT? REALLY?! OH, YOU POOR THING! HOW ABSOLUTELY TERRIBLE!

ER, ARE YOU SURE YOU'RE FEELING OKAY? IT'S NOT LIKE YOU TO BE POLITE, AND YOU HAVE JUST BEEN BLOWN UP.

HMM, NOW YOU COME TO MENTION IT...

PAT WAFT

NOOOO!! I AM NOT OKAY! I AM FURIOUS!!!

WILL ONE OF YOU IDIOTS OBEY MY RANTING AND RE-CAPTURE THAT RIDICULOUS-LOOKING CRIMINAL!?!

ER, WHICH CRIMINAL WOULD THAT BE, YOUR CRUELNESS?

YEAH, ALL THE PRISONERS DUE TO BE HANGED HAVE ESCAPED... AND ACTUALLY, WHEN YOU THINK ABOUT IT, A LOT OF US BROILERDOOMIANS LOOK A BIT RIDICULOUS ... SEE?

OI! I'M AS PRETTY AS A PICTURE!

WELL THEN, YOU'D BETTER SEIZE EVERYONE, BEFORE I DIP YOU IN WAX, PAINT YOU RED, SET LIGHT TO YOUR EARS AND USE YOU AS A FESTIVE CANDLE!!!

NO TIME FOR DAWDLING, DON - YOU'RE ABOUT TO HAVE THE ENTIRE CITY ON YOUR HEELS!

GULP! NO CHANGE THERE, THEN! OKAY, CASTANET - HERE WE GO!!!

THE USUAL PURPOSE OF CASTLE FORTIFICATIONS IS TO KEEP THE ENEMY **OUT**.

UNFORTUNATELY FOR DON – AND THE LONG-SUFFERING CITIZENS OF CORPSE CITY – GENERAL SPODE MAINTAINS A QUITE *DIFFERENT* VIEW.

IT IS SPODE'S BELIEF THAT TALL WALLS, BOILING OIL AND ARMED GUARDS ARE THERE TO KEEP THE CASTLE POPULATION **IN**.

AFTER ALL, IF EVERYONE WERE FREE TO LEAVE, WHO WOULD BRING HIM BREAKFAST IN BED?

COR, THIS IS MORE ENTERTAINING THAN THE CIRCUS!

STOP CLOWNING AROUND AND HELP OUT, BEFORE SPODE MAKES **YOU** THE STAR OF HIS NEXT SHOW!

AGH!! FORGET MY ORDERS, MEN! DO NOT, I REPEAT, DO **NOT** FOLLOW ME!!

'JOIN THE ARMY', THEY SAID, 'SCALE THE PROMOTIONAL LADDER', THEY SAID...

NOT TO MAKE *LIGHT* OF THE SITUATION, BUT *WATER* WAY TO SPEND A MORNING, EH?

THAT'S ENOUGH OF THAT, SON!! YOU'RE FANNING THE FLAMES OF MY IRRITATION!

PUFF... SAFINA! I CAN'T BELIEVE YOU'VE SAVED OUR SKIN! *AGAIN!*

WELL, I DON'T INTEND TO MAKE A HABIT OF IT. BESIDES, WE'RE NOT FREE YET...

NOW, BE HONEST – DO YOU TRUST ME?

OF *COURSE* I TRUST YOU!

TRUST CAN BE EARNED, DON, AND IT CAN BE LOST. AND KNOWING HOW MUCH CASTANET HATES FLYING, I'M PRETTY CONFIDENT I'M ABOUT TO LOSE HIS.

F-FLYING ... DID YOU SAY **FLYING?** ARE YOU *INSANE,* SEÑORITA?! I'D RATHER TAKE MY CHANCES WITH **SPODE!**

IS THAT WHAT I THINK IT– ER ... WHAT *IS* THAT?

IT'S **DANGER**, DON! IT'S **DOOOOOOM!** IT'S THE END OF OUR LITTLE *LIVES!*

ACTUALLY IT'S OUR TICKET TO FREEDOM! **VIKTOR** INVENTED THIS MARVELLOUS FLYING MACHINE FOR OCCASIONS JUST LIKE THESE!

HEY – WHAT DO YOU CALL THESE THINGS, HUH? **CHOPPED LIVER?** DON'T YOU THINK IF I *WANTED* TO FLY ANYWHERE I'D BE FIRST IN LINE?!

STOP MOANING, TAKE A LOOK DOWN THERE, AND *THEN* TELL ME YOU STILL WANT TO STAY.

ARCHERRRS! TAKE AIM!

THREE HUNDRED FEET, FROM A RAISED POSITION, THROUGH A BIG CROWD... THAT'S SOME *FANCY BOW* WORK!

YES, YES, BUT WHY DID SHE HAVE TO HIT *MY* HAT?

I STILL WANT TO STAY! I STILL WANT TO STAY!

TOUGH LUCK, FEATHERS! YOU'RE COMING WITH US AND THAT'S FINAL!

OKAY, SO HOW DOES THIS CONTRAPTION WORK?

HOP!

LEAP!

WORK? UM. YES. WELL, I'VE NAMED IT THE 'UPSY-DOWNSY' AFTER CASTANET'S FAVOURITE DRINK. SEE, WE START *UP*...

...AND THEN WE FALL **DOOOWN!**

AHHHHHHH!!

ARCHERRRRS! LOOSE!!

WOOOMP!

NOT QUITE THE LIFT I WAS HOPING FOR BUT THAT'S DONE THE TRICK!

SERIOUSLY, I DEFINITELY 'EARD SOMEONE SAY 'JUMP' THAT TIME.

SORRY, CASTANET, WE'RE TRAVELLING TOO FAST TO JUMP! HOLD ON AND HOPE FOR THE BEST!

OH, GREAT ... THE IRREGULARS' MOTTO...

FLOOMPH!

THE PIECE OF CAKE BAKERY

WHERE ARE YOUR MANNERS, BERNARDO? GUESTS DROP IN FOR BREAKFAST AND YOU JUST STAND THERE GAWPING!

QUITE RIGHT, DEAR, QUITE RIGHT! ER ... TEA, ANYONE? CINNAMON BUN?

PATHETIC EFFORT, VALUSH! THEY GOT AWAY ... SO NO NEW HEADWEAR FOR YOU!

YOUR TIGHT-FISTED STINGYNESS KNOWS NO BOUNDS, MASTER.

MY, MY...

SOMEONE SEEMS TO HAVE BEEN HAVING FUN IN MY ABSENCE.

REGINA, MY PRECOCIOUS PICCOLO, YOU'RE LOOKING A LITTLE WINDSWEPT! WHERE DID YOU COME FROM?

OH, UM, I JUST DROPPED IN TO CHECK ON THE MORNING EXECUTIONS! EVERYTHING GO TO PLAN?

NO, IT MOST CERTAINLY DID NOT, BUT THAT'S A PROBLEM I SHALL SOON RESOLVE! THERE IS ONLY ONE NEST OF RATS FOOLISH ENOUGH TO HIDE THESE DESPERADOS...

...SO I THINK IT'S HIGH TIME CORPSE CITY DECLARED WAR ON THE DEMON DRINK AND THOSE IRRITATING IRREGULARS!!

NEWS OF THEIR IMMINENT DESTRUCTION TRAVELS FAST. AS A RESULT, LATER THAT DAY, ONE RESIDENT OF THE DEMON DRINK EXPRESSES HIS OUTRAGE IN A TRIED AND TESTED MANNER...

The Demon Drink
CURES WHAT ALES YOU!

THAT NO GOOD 🌀✨🗡️🦇💣 TYRANNICAL TYKE! HOW DARE HE TRY AND EXECUTE MY FRIENDS?! I'VE HALF A MIND TO STORM HIS CITY AND 💀✖️💥⚡

THUNK!

WHUNK!

CARICATURES! JUST LIKE YOU = $1 BETTER THAN YOU = $2

IF I GET MY HANDS ON HIM I'LL 💀✂️🍩🌀💣☁️✦✦💥

CLOSED DUE TO HITHERTO UNFORESEEN PREPARATIONS FOR BATTLE!

BAM! SHUNNK!

PANT! ... PANT!

SIT DOWN AND CALM DOWN, LEWD! NOT EVERY PROBLEM CAN BE SOLVED BY THROWING A WEAPON!

SOME OF THE BEST ONES CAN! BACK WHEN I WAS A MARSH RANGER, I HAD THIS EPIC DUEL WITH A TEN-LEGGED SCARAB BEETLE CALLED FRANKY CHIP FINGERS. THROWING AN AXE SURE SOLVED THAT PROBLEM!

SNIFF... I MISS THAT AXE...

MOVING ON, IT'S TIME WE FACED THE FACTS - GENERAL SPODE WILL SOON BE COMING FOR THE IRREGULARS! AND HE WILL NOT BE COMING ALONE!

CLAP! CLAP!

NOW, IN TIMES OF CRISIS THERE'S NO SUCH THING AS A BAD IDEA, SO LET'S HEAR YOUR THOUGHTS!

43

WHY DON'T WE JUST *HIDE?* HIDING ALWAYS WORKS FOR ME! WHEN MY FEATHERS GET WET I CAN FIT IN SURPRISINGLY SMALL SPACES.

TURNS OUT THERE *IS* SUCH A THING AS A BAD IDEA. 'HIDING' IS *NOT A PLAN, YOU FEATHERED TWIT!* IT'S WHAT YOU DO WHEN YOU CAN'T *THINK* OF A PLAN.

I SAY WE ARM OURSELVES TO THE TEETH, WING AND HOOK, AND WE *FIGHT!* WE SHOULD SHOW THAT 💀☠️ 🖕 AND HIS ROTTEN ☠️ ARMY *EXACTLY* WHAT WE'RE MADE OF!

ER, DO YOU MEAN YOUR BLOOD AND GUTS AND BONES AND GIZZARDS AND STUFF?

NO, THAT'S **NOT** WHAT I MEAN, VIKTOR, AND YOU KNOW IT! I'M NOT SHOWING *ANYONE* MY GIZZARDS! THIS CROW HAS SOME DIGNITY!

THIS CROW ALSO HAS A MIGHTY THIRST!

SIGH ... WHAT DO *YOU* THINK, DON?

ME?

I *THINK* ALL OUR PROBLEMS ARE **MY** FAULT! I *THINK* YOU'RE INJURED BECAUSE OF A RESCUE YOU WOULDN'T HAVE NEEDED TO PERFORM IF *I* HADN'T GOT INVOLVED! I THINK ... I THINK...

...I THINK I WANT TO GO HOME.

¡AYAYAY! LET'S NOT THROW THE CHICK OUT THE TREE, CHICO! IT WAS *ME* THAT DROPPED THE BRUSH, REMEMBER! STILL GOT THE PAINT ON MY TUSH TO PROVE IT!

AND THESE ARE JUST *SCRATCHES!* YOU'RE NOT TO BLAME FOR WHAT'S HAPPENING - SPODE HAS BEEN ITCHING FOR A SCRAP FOR AGES. YOU'RE JUST HIS LATEST EXCUSE.

HOP!

THAT'S SETTLED THEN! NOW, I DON'T CARE FOR SPEECHES BUT I CARE A **LOT** ABOUT SWORDS, SO TAKE YOUR PICK! DON, I RECOMMEND THIS TRUSTY *EMBALMER!* IT MUMMIFIES YOUR ENEMIES ON CONTACT!

OOOOOH! BLESS THOSE PHARAOHS AND THEIR SORCERER'S WAYS...

?!

MUMMIFICATION... MUMMIFY... MUMMIES... **MUM!!!**

BUMP!

KA-

BOOOOOOM!

GAH!! I HOPE FOR YOUR SAKE MY **EYEBROWS** GROW BACK!!

SORRY, CASTANET, BUT I JUST REALISED THAT I'VE BEEN HERE FOR **DAYS** AND I HAVEN'T THOUGHT ONCE ABOUT MY FAMILY! WHAT'S... **WHAT'S THE MATTER WITH ME?!**

PAT PAT PAT

NOTHING, THAT'S HOW BROILERDOOM SNARES YOU. IT WILL SLOWLY **DRAIN** AWAY YOUR MEMORIES, **UNLESS** YOU KEEP HOLD OF SOMETHING FROM YOUR OLD WORLD – LIKE MY LOST **NECKLACE**, WHICH YOU MAGICALLY FOUND...

...OR **THIS** STRANGE GARMENT WHICH I PLUCKED FROM THE TICKLE YOUR FANCY (DRESS) WASTE BIN.

MY SCHOOL TIE! AND NOT A SOUP STAIN TO BE SEEN!

YOU RISKED YOUR OWN NECK TO SAVE ME FROM THE GALLOWS BECAUSE OF A **NECKLACE?**

YOU DID RUN OFF BEFORE I COULD THANK YOU FOR RETURNING IT, BUT **NO** – I SAVED YOU BECAUSE I **LIKE** YOU, YOU CHALK-HAIRED TWIT! NOW, WE'VE A BIG BATTLE TO WIN AND A SMALL GRUBBY BAR TO PROTECT SO JUST MAKE SURE YOU KEEP THAT 'TIE' CLOSE. IT'S YOUR **LIFELINE!**

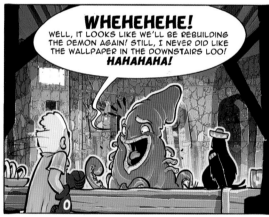

WHEHEHEHE! WELL, IT LOOKS LIKE WE'LL BE REBUILDING THE DEMON AGAIN! STILL, I NEVER DID LIKE THE WALLPAPER IN THE DOWNSTAIRS LOO! **HAHAHAHA!**

HOW CAN YOU BE SO JOLLY, VIKTOR? WE'RE ALL ABOUT TO BE BURIED RIGHT NEXT TO THAT HORRIBLE WALLPAPER!

NO, NO – NOT ALL... NOT **YOU** ANYWAY. YOU DID SAY YOU WANTED TO LEAVE, RIGHT?

WHAT WITH THE COMING MASSACRE AND EVERYTHING, **THIS** SEEMS TO ME LIKE THE PERFECT MOMENT TO SHOW YOU THE WAY BACK **HOME!**

THE WHAT?!!

ARE YOU **SERIOUS?!** I'VE BEEN RUNNING AND FIGHTING AND STRUGGLING TO SURVIVE WHEN I COULD HAVE SIMPLY **LEFT?!** AND YOU COULD HAVE TOLD ME THIS **WHENEVER YOU WANTED?!**

NO, NO ... NOT **WHENEVER**... ONLY WHEN IT WAS **FUNNY! WHAHAHA!** THE SECRET OF COMEDY IS IN THE **TIMING,** RIGHT?

BUT MY LIFE IS NOT A **JOKE!**

YOU ARE AWARE THAT YOUR BEST FRIEND IS A TALKING CROW WHO JUST LOST HIS EYEBROWS?

VIKTOR'S GOT A POINT – AND **I'M** STILL SMILING!

ANYWAY, I LIKE TO THINK OF COMEDY AND TRAGEDY AS A SINGLE HAT THAT SHADES YOU FROM BOTH THE SUN **AND** THE RAIN! **HA!** NOW FOLLOW ME!

WHAT DOES THAT EVEN **MEAN?**

SHUNK!

CLICK!

IGNORE MY BABBLING, DON – I ALWAYS **BABBLE** WHEN I'M EXCITED ... AND I'M **ALWAYS** EXCITED! BETTER WATCH YOUR STEP DOWN HERE. I DROPPED A PEANUT BUTTER SANDWICH A FEW DECADES AGO AND I THINK IT'S **GONE OFF...**

UNBELIEVABLE! WHERE ARE WE, VIKTOR?

WHY, THE UNDERWORLD-RENOWNED **RIKTUS BIBLIOTHECA,** OF COURSE! ISN'T IT OBVIOUS?

FOR **THREE CENTURIES** I HAVE PAINSTAKINGLY GATHERED THE RAREST SECRETS OF BROILERDOOM AND STORED THEM IN MY LIBRARY OF WONDERS!

REALLY? AND I SUPPOSE **THESE** ARE 'PRECIOUS'?

YEP – AND **RARE!** THAT'S A FIRST EDITION! YOU CAN TELL A LOT ABOUT A SQUIDY BY THE QUALITY OF HIS **COMIC COLLECTION!**

I'VE BEEN HERE A **LONG** TIME, DON, BUT THERE IS STILL MUCH ABOUT THIS UNDERWORLD I DON'T UNDERSTAND. THE **UNENDING FOG** SURROUNDS CORPSE CITY TO THE NORTH AND THE EAST, WHILE OUR SLUMS ARE HEMMED IN BY THE **ARRIVAL PLAINS...**

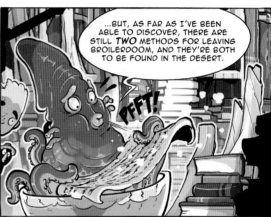

...BUT, AS FAR AS I'VE BEEN ABLE TO DISCOVER, THERE ARE STILL **TWO** METHODS FOR LEAVING BROILERDOOM, AND THEY'RE BOTH TO BE FOUND IN THE DESERT.

PFFT!

ALL RIGHT, SO WHAT'S OPTION **ONE?**

EASY ... SIMPLY **GET YOURSELF KILLED!** WHA-HAHA!

TRUST AN OLD CON ARTIST, CHICO – YOU **NEVER** ACCEPT THE FIRST OFFER! HOLD OUT FOR THE **BIG** GIFT.

AGREED! OKAY ... UM... OPTION **TWO?**

LET ME SEE... OH YES, THIS IS **MUCH** HARDER... AND JUST AS LIKELY TO GET YOU KILLED!

I'M STARTING TO GET USED TO THOSE ODDS! WHAT EXACTLY DO I HAVE TO **DO?**

'GREET YOUR FATE LIKE AN OLD FRIEND.' ALL THE REST OF THE INSTRUCTIONS ARE IN HERE! NOW, IF YOU DON'T MIND I'VE SOME RATHER LARGE BARRICADES TO BUILD BEFORE SPODE ARRIVES! **WHEHEHE!**

RIDDLES AND MAPS ... SIGH... UNLIKE OUR ESCAPE FROM CORPSE CITY, THIS REALLY **DOES** LOOKS LIKE A ONE-WAY TRIP. CASTANET, I WON'T BLAME YOU IF YOU DECIDE TO STAY.

DON, YOU ARE RAPIDLY BECOMING MY **NUMBER ONE AMIGO!** I'M WITH YOU TO THE VERY END. AND BESIDES, WITH EVERYONE HARD AT **WAR** WHO **ELSE** IS GOING TO WATCH YOUR BACK?

AND SO, WITH THE BRIEFEST 'ADIOS', OUR INTREPID DUO LEAVE THE *COMFORT* ... ERM... THE *SAFETY* ... UM... WELL, THEY LEAVE THE SLUMS!

GASP ... I CAN HANDLE THE SAND BETWEEN MY CLAWS, BUT BLACK FEATHERS AND WARM WEATHER DO *NOT* MIX!

AT LEAST *YOU'VE* GOT A SOMBRERO!

OKAY THEN... ...*PUFF*... THAT SCROLL OF VIKTOR'S ... IS IT LEADING US ON SOME *SUPER SECRET SAFE* PATH THROUGH THE DESERT?

ER ... NOT... EXACTLY. IN FACT, ONE MIGHT SAY QUITE THE *OPPOSITE!*

GRAAAAAAAAAAAAAH!

¡HOSTÍA! AND *THAT'S* OUR CUE TO *VAMOOSH!* YOU KNOW THE DRILL - LEFT FOOT, RIGHT FOOT AND YOUR BODY WILL FOLLOW!!!

NO.

'NO'?! WHAT DO YOU MEAN 'NO'? THIS IS NOT A 'NO' MOMENT!!

HAVE YOU *EVER* WONDERED - HAS *ANYONE* EVER WONDERED - WHAT MIGHT HAPPEN IF YOU *DIDN'T* RUN FROM THE 'HORRIBLE SMELLY GREAT MEANY', AS YOU SO NICELY PUT IT?

¡HOOOOOOOOOOMPH!

O-ONLY IN F-FEVERED, B-BLOOD-CURDLING *NIGHTMARES!!*

WELL, IN THAT CASE, LITTLE BUDDY ... *GULP*... I GUESS YOU AND I ARE GOING TO BE THE *FIRST* TO FIND OUT!

S-S-SO M-M-MANY T-T-TOMBSTONE SH-SHAPED T-T-T-TEETH...!

P-PERHAPS THIS WASN'T S-SUCH A G-G-GREAT IDEA!

...T-T-T-TEETH...

WHAT DID VIKTOR SAY?! WHAT DID VIKTOR SAY?! 'GREET YOUR FATE LIKE AN OLD FRIEND!' OKAY, HERE GOES ... AHEM... HELLO, MISTER ER WORM! HOW ARE YOU? UM IT'S BEEN TOO LONG!

...T-T-T-TEETH...

P-P-PLEASE DON'T EAT US!!

SURELY YOU KNOW IT'S RUDE FOR OLD FRIENDS TO EAT EACH OTHER? BUT YES, DON, IT'S BEEN FAR TOO LONG.

MEANWHILE, BACK IN KRAPOOKERVILLE, GENERAL SPODE IS RIDING HIGH ON THE THOUGHT OF VICTORY...

BY THE ORDER OF ME, I HEREBY DECLARE THE PROPERTY KNOWN AS **THE DEMON DRINK** TO BE AN ABOMINATION ON THE FACE OF BROILERDOOM AND I CONDEMN IT TO **IMMEDIATE DESTRUCTION!** THE SAME GOES FOR ANY RESIDENT WHO CHOOSES **NOT** TO SURRENDER IN THE NEXT TEN SECONDS!

SIGH ... YOU KNOW, I'VE FOUGHT THESE **IRREGULARS** BEFORE. I BET YOU A MONTH'S WAGES THAT THIS LITTLE ENCOUNTER ENDS WITH SOMETHING NASTY HAPPENING TO US!

BOOOM!

WHAT? TWO GOLD BITS AND A HAIRCUT? **YOU'RE ON!** WE CAN'T **POSSIBLY** LOSE – OLD SPODE'S BROUGHT MOST OF THE CITY GUARD AND HE'S IN A **TYRANNICAL** MOOD!

BOOOM!

SPEAK UP NOW – WHAT DO YOU FOOLS HAVE TO SAY TO MY GENEROUS OFFER?

WE SAY **NUTS** TO THAT, YOU CRUSTY

LEWD, OTHER THAN FRUITY LANGUAGE, WHAT IS OUR STRATEGY HERE?!

BOOM! BOOOM!

YOU AND VIKTOR ARE GOING TO START BY POURING LAST MONTH'S LEFTOVER STEW ON THEIR HEADS – MARROW'S BEEN SAVING IT FOR JUST SUCH AN OCCASION!

GAHH!! GROSS!

BWAHAHAHA! I HEARD THAT! **KITCHEN SCRAPS?!** MY SOLDIERS ARE NOT SCARED OF A FEW MOULDY TITBITS!

ER, P-P-PERMISSION TO BE **VERY** SCARED, S-S-SIR? I'VE EATEN THE DEMON S-S-STEW AND IT'S PRETTY M-M-MURDEROUS WHEN IT'S **FRESH!**

SIGH... THERE'S NOTHING WORSE THAN WINNING A BET THAT ENDS IN YOUR OWN DEATH...

STOP!!

PLEASE, SPODE - I KNOW WE'VE HAD OUR DIFFERENCES, BUT YOU MUST STOP THIS MADNESS! YOUR WAR-MAKING IS BOTHERING MY BEGONIAS!

?!

NOW, I'VE ASSEMBLED YOU A LOVELY LITTLE 'GIVE PEACE A CHANCE' FRUIT BASKET OFFERING! THE POMEGRANATES ARE DELICIOUS, AND AS FOR THE KUMQUATS...

WHAT IS IT WITH YOU BLITHERING NITS AND YOUR POMEGRANATES? NOBODY LIKES THEM!

RIPLEY, YOU ARE MY SWORN RIVAL! YOU'LL NEVER FIND PEACE WHILE I RULE THE SLUMS AND YOUR CRIMINAL FRIENDS CONTINUE TO MOCK ME! IN THE PAST TWO DAYS MY MEN AND I HAVE BEEN MADE TO LOOK LIKE FOOLS MORE TIMES THAN I CARE TO REMEMBER!

FIVE AND COUNTING!

CAN WE DISPENSE WITH THE PREAMBLE, MY LORD? I'D RATHER LIKE TO SKIP TO THE PART WHERE I SKEWER THE ONE WHO SHOT MY HAT!

DID SOMEONE CALL?

TWANG!

WHAT THE...?!! AGHHH!! SHE'S DONE IT AGAIN!!

THAT'S THE SIGNAL, LADS! UP AND AT 'EM! FOR THE DEMON! FOR THE SLUMS! FOR BROILERDOOM!

CHAAAAAAAAAAAAARGE!!

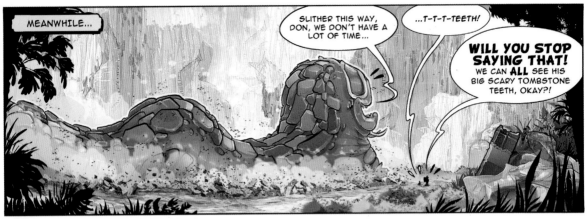

MEANWHILE...

SLITHER THIS WAY, DON, WE DON'T HAVE A LOT OF TIME...

...T-T-T-TEETH!

WILL YOU STOP **SAYING THAT!** WE CAN **ALL** SEE HIS BIG SCARY TOMBSTONE TEETH, OKAY?!

ERM, I **THINK** I KNOW HOW THIS WORKS. VIKTOR GAVE ME THIS SCROLL AND IT EXPLAINS ALL ABOUT THE BROILERDOOM EXITS...

IT'S **YOU**, ISN'T IT? **YOU'RE** THE DOORWAY HOME.

I PREFER THE NAME **THANATOS** TO 'DOORWAY' - OR 'WORM' FOR THAT MATTER - BUT YES, YOU'RE A SMART BOY. SEEMS **THEY** WERE RIGHT ABOUT YOU...

THEY? WHO ARE **THEY?**

OH, YOUR GRAND ADVENTURE IS GOING TO RAISE A **LOT** OF QUESTIONS, BUT I'VE ONLY TIME TO ANSWER **ONE**. YES, THERE **IS** A PORTAL BACK HOME BURIED WITHIN MY IMPENETRABLE HIDE. MANY HAVE TRIED TO CUT IT OUT AND FAILED, AS YOU CAN SEE. ACCESS IS... **RATHER EXTREME!**

BUT TELL ME, DON, HOW IMPORTANT IS IT THAT YOU LEAVE AT THIS **PRECISE** MOMENT?

ERM ... IMPORTANT ENOUGH THAT I'D RISK MEETING **YOU.**

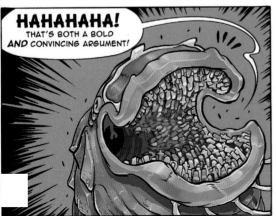

HAHAHAHA! THAT'S BOTH A BOLD **AND** CONVINCING ARGUMENT!

HOLD THE TACOS A MOMENT ... YOU'RE LOSING ME! WHAT DO YOU MEAN **HE** IS THE DOOR?

THERE'S A WAY OUT, CASTANET! A WAY BACK TO MY FAMILY AND FRIENDS, AND IT'S HIDDEN IN THIS MONSTER'S **GUTS!** ALL I HAVE TO DO IS ALLOW MYSELF TO BE **EATEN ALIVE!**

EATEN *ALIVE?* ... HMMM ...

THAT'S IT, AMIGO, JUST TAKE YOUR TIME...

...ANY SECOND NOW...

POP! POP! POP!

EATEN ALIVEEEE!!! WHAT IN THE NAME OF CHOCOLATE CUPCAKES WAS I *THINKING?!!!*

...AAAAAND HE'S BACK!

I REFUSE TO EAT YOU, DON. *THE MUNCHING* IS A SACRED RITUAL, AND CAN *ONLY* BE PERFORMED ON THOSE WITH NO REASON LEFT TO LIVE. DOES THAT SOUND LIKE YOU?

NO, I GUESS NOT ... THERE'S SAFINA AND LEWD AND THE OTHERS ... BUT WHAT HELP CAN I BE? THIS IS ALL SUCH A *BIG* MESS AND I'M JUST ONE BOY!

AH, WELL, PERHAPS *I* CAN BE OF ASSISTANCE. IT'S BEEN A LIFETIME SINCE I LAST WENT TO TOWN.

IN THAT CASE, WE'RE *ALL* GOING BACK AND SPODEY BETTER GET READY ... THE OLD TERRIFIED DON IS *LONG GONE!*

BUT AT THIS PRECISE MOMENT, DON'S NEMESIS IS OCCUPIED WITH RATHER MORE *PRESSING* TACTICAL CONCERNS...

I'M RUNNING OUT OF STEW, LEWD, BUT I'M NOT RUNNING OUT OF *TARGETS!*

GIVE 'EM WHAT FOR, BOYS, PUSH WITH ALL YOUR MIGHT!!

PUT YOUR BACKS INTO IT, MEN! CRUSH THESE FOOLS!!

GAHHH!! IT SMELLS LIKE A WET DOG!!

SIGH ... THERE MUST BE ANOTHER WAY TO RESOLVE THIS PREDICAMENT. VIOLENCE CAN'T BE THE *ONLY* SOLUTION.

THUMP!

SLAMM!

WHAT ABOUT IF WE ALL SIT DOWN AND SETTLE OUR DIFFERENCES OVER A JUICY ROAST WITH ALL THE TRIMMINGS? I'LL EVEN BREAK OUT MY RARE HONEYGUM MUSTARD!

RIPLEY! WE'RE IN THE MIDDLE OF THE FIGHT OF OUR LIVES! WHO WANTS TO STOP A FIGHT IN THE *MIDDLE?!*

W-W-WE D-DO!!!

B.R.E.

BUT YOU *COULD* STILL HELP TO END THIS BATTLE. REMEMBER THE DAY YOU QUIT THE IRREGULARS? YOU GAVE ME 'BRENDA' FOR SAFE KEEPING AND, WELL, I'VE BEEN KEEPING HER VERY SAFE EVER SINCE.

B.R.E.N.D.A.

PERHAPS NOW MIGHT BE A RATHER GOOD TIME TO —

NO! KEEP THAT THING AWAY FROM ME! I'LL NOT BECOME THAT MONSTER AGAIN!

POM!

B.R.E.N.D.A.

LEWD, LEAVE RIPLEY WITH HIS PERSONAL DEMONS AND GET OVER HERE! WE'RE ABOUT TO HAVE SOME PRETTY SERIOUS COMPANY!

MAKE YOUR GENERAL PROUD, MEN! NOW IS THE HOUR FOR *BRAVERY* AND *HEROISM!*

...SAYS THE BRAVE HERO STANDING AT THE *BACK!*

WOO HOO! FRESH MEAT! THIS SHOULD BE FUN!

WE'RE OUTNUMBERED THIRTY TO ONE! FOR WHOM IS THIS GOING TO BE FUN?!

SUCH RECKLESS TACTICS CAN PROVE TO BE REMARKABLY EFFECTIVE.

CRASH!

MUNCH! CRUNCH! CHOMP!

THEY'RE **EATING** THE **BARRICADES!** OUR **DEFENCES** ARE FALLING! THE **GREEDY FIENDS** ARE **EVERYWHERE!**

SQUAWK!

?

HE'LL HAVE A ROOT BEER.

IT'S NO GOOD, LEWD — THERE ARE TOO MANY OF THEM! GRAB RIPLEY AND HEAD FOR THE HIGH GROUND!!

BUT ... BUT I WAS **WINNING!**

NO, NO, NO ... YOU DON'T GET TO **RETREAT!** DIDN'T ANYONE TELL YOU — THIS IS A **LAST STAND!** I EVEN BROUGHT AN ARTIST TO CAPTURE THE MOMENT ON CANVAS!

I WON'T LAST IF I HAVE TO **STAND** AND PAINT ALL THIS. MAY I SIT?

HURHURHUR! IF YOU MONKEYS HAVE ANY FINAL WORDS, NOW'S THE TIME TO **SPIT 'EM OUT!**

PTOOOA!

WOW — WHAT AN UNFORTUNATE EXPRESSION TO HAVE CHOSEN! HOW ABOUT 'DUCK'?

DUCK? WHAT DO YOU —

TOCK!

RuJOOOAR!!

NICE SHOT, PAL!

?!

!!

The Demon Drink

?

THERE'S SOMETHING YOU DON'T SEE EVERY DAY!

DON?

WHAT THE—

I'M SORRY, SPODE, DIDN'T ANYONE TELL YOU? THIS IS WHAT HAPPENS AT AN IRREGULARS LAST STAND!

OOOH... I CAN SEE MY HOUSE FROM UP HERE!

PtooIE!

THAMMP!

AGH! RUN AWAY!!! REGROUP!! EVERYONE TAKE COVER!!

LOOKS LIKE THEY'RE TRYING TO HIDE ... BUT ISN'T THAT CHEATING?

YES, IT IS! OKAY, THANATOS — LET'S BREAK OUT THE BIG GUN...

BOOOMPH!

THE BROILERDOOM BELLY-FLOP!!!

WAIT A SECOND, ...*NGGN*... THE SHOW'S NOT OVER! THERE'S STILL WORK TO BE DONE...